PONIES LOVE PETS!

ORCHARD BOOKS

First published in the US in 2014 by Little, Brown and Company
This edition first published in the UK in 2018 by The Watts Publishing Group

1 3 5 7 9 10 8 6 4 2

A CIP catalogue record for this book is available from the British Library.

ISBN 978 1 40835 239 7

Printed and bound in China

Orchard Books
An imprint of Hachette Children's Group
Part of The Watts Publishing Group Limited
Carmelite House
50 Victoria Embankment
London EC4Y 0DZ

An Hachette UK Company
www.hachette.co.uk

www.hachettechildrens.co.uk

PONIES LOVE PETS!

by Emily C. Hughes

ORCHARD

Meet the Ponies and their pets!

Twilight and
Owlowiscious

Rarity
and Opal

Pinkie Pie and
Gummy

Look for these words when you read this book. Can you spot them all?

alligator

cow

tortoise

phoenix

These ponies are best friends.

They love to laugh together.

They also love to play with their pets!

The ponies and their pets are
always there to help one another.

Angel is Fluttershy's pet bunny.

He can be a bit bossy.

But Angel makes Fluttershy
feel better when she is sad.

Pinkie Pie has a pet alligator named Gummy.
Most ponies would not want an alligator
for a pet, but Gummy is special.
He has no teeth!

It is lucky because he LOVES to bite!

Twilight Sparkle has Owlowiscious. He helps her by bringing books from the library.

At first, he and Spike did not get along,
but now they are good friends.

Applejack has a dog called Winona.

Winona helps Applejack herd the cows.

Applejack got Winona
when she was a puppy.
She loves to run and leap and
have her belly scratched!

Rainbow Dash wants a pet as fast and cool as she is, like a falcon or a bat.

She has a contest to find the best animal.
Fluttershy has lots of ideas.

Soon Rainbow Dash meets Tank.

Tank is a tortoise.

Tank may be slow,
but Rainbow Dash fixes that.
She turns him into a flying tortoise!

Opalescence is Rarity's cat.
She helps make beautiful
dresses for the other ponies.

The cat does not like to get wet.

She also does not like to do chores.

Opal hates it when someone tries
to steal her toys!

It is not just the ponies of Ponyville
who have pets.
Princess Celestia has a phoenix
named Philomena.
Philomena has a special talent.

She can burst into flames!

Philomena sometimes uses her
talent to play tricks on the ponies.
Fluttershy has never seen
anything like it!

Even Spike has a pet.

Peewee is a baby phoenix.

Spike rescued Peewee
when he was still an egg.

Pets are hard work!

But the ponies love them.

And the pets love the ponies!

Because friendship is magic, and
pets are a very special kind of friend!